CAMPFIRE SONGS

ACKNOWLEDGEMENTS :

Ron Branagan   for yet another totally appropriate cover. (He's the bottom left of the back cover!)

Henry Dean for the cartoons and our friend Lightning, the Mod conductor. "If you knew Henry ... "

Paul Taylor for making the music understandable.

Introduction

This book is published as a sequel to 'Camp Fire Stunts', which has been enthusiastically received across the country. In 'Camp Fire Songs' we have attempted to bring together a number of well-known and less well-known songs which would go down well at any camp fire and many other light entertainment occasions. As far as we are aware, all of the songs have their origins in the mists of time, and we have, therefore, not credited them to any one person. If we have inadvertently infringed copyright, we apologise in advance and would be happy to make a correction in a future edition!

We have divided the songs into a number of different sections for ease of reference and there is an index at the back of the book. A well balanced camp fire will contain songs from many of the sections and a good camp fire leader will have a basic outline to the programme in mind, but will also have a number of spare songs up his sleeve, should the mood of the camp fire tend in any one direction.

It has been difficult to select a comparatively small number of songs for this book from the many hundreds available. We hope to be able to publish further books of camp fire songs and, indeed, stunts, and would be very pleased to receive examples of your favourite songs and stunts.

The address to write to is :

PRINTFORCE
6 ANGEL HILL DRIVE
SUTTON
SM1 3BX

Contents

This is Lightning, our mod conductor.
He will appear from time to time,
particularly to help you with the
action songs.

Beginnings and endings

WE'RE ALL TOGETHER AGAIN

We're all together again, we're here, we're here
We're all together again, we're here, we're here
And who knows when we'll be all together again
Singing we're all together again, we're here
                                                    we're here

CAMP FIRE'S BURNING

Camp fire's burning, camp fire's burning
Draw nearer, draw nearer
In the gloaming, in the gloaming
Come sing and be merry

Note :- This can be sung as a round in 4 parts,
*   starting at A, B, C and D respectively.*

IT'S A GOOD TIME TO GET ACQUAINTED

(Tune : Tipperary)

It's a good time to get acquainted
It's a good time to know
Who is sitting close beside you
And to smile and say "Hello"
Goodbye, chilly feeling
Goodbye, glassy stare
If we all join hands and pull together
We're sure to get there

IT'S GREAT FUN TO JOIN A CUB PACK

(Tune : Tipperary)

It is great fun to join a Cub Pack
It is great fun you bet
For the Cub gang leads to the Scout gang
On your marks boys now get set
Hurrah for Akela - Hi-ki, hi-ki, hi
It is great fun to join a Cub Pack
Hi-ki, hi-ki, hi

WE'RE HERE FOR FUN

(Tune : Auld Lang Syne)

We're here for fun right from the start
So drop your dignity
Just laugh and sing with all your heart
And show your loyalty
May all your troubles be forgot
May this night be the best
Join in the songs we sing tonight
Be happy with the rest

AULD LANG SYNE

Should auld acquaintance be forgot
And never brought to min'?
Should auld acquaintance be forgot
And days o'lang syne?

For auld lang syne, my dear
For auld lang syne   (CHORUS)
We'll take a cup o' kindness yet
For auld lang syne

We twa hae run about the braes
And pu'd the gowans fine
But we've wander'd mony a weary foot
Sin' auld lang syne

CHORUS

We twa hae paid-l't in the burn
Frae morning sun till dine
But seas between us braid hae roar'd
Sin' auld lang syne

CHORUS

And there's a hand, my trusty frien'
And gie's a hand o' thine
And we'll tak' a right gude willy-waught
For auld lang syne

CHORUS

And surely ye'll be your pint stoup
And surely I'll be mine!
And we'll tak' a cup o' kindness yet
For auld lang syne

CHORUS

GOING DOWN THE VALLEY

We are going down the valley
Going down the valley
Going down the valley, one by one, one by one
We are going down the valley
Going down the valley
Going to the setting of the sun

We are coming up the valley
Coming up the valley
Coming up the valley one by one, one by one
We are coming up the valley
Coming up the valley
Coming to the rising of the sun

The first line of the first verse should be sung
loudly and the song should be sung progressively
quieter, to give an indication of the party moving
away down the valley. The second verse should
start very quietly and should get louder and louder
as the party returns.

IN MY FATHER'S HOUSE

Oh come and go with me (allelujah)
To my father's house (allelujah)
To my father's house (allelujah)
To my father's house
Oh come and go with me (allelujah)
To my father's house
Where there's peace (forever) peace (forever peace)

Verse 2 :

There's sweet communion there   allelujah

Verse 3 :

There'll be no parting there   allelujah

Downward tails in
music refer to words
in brackets - optional
second part

Action Songs

MY HAT IT HAS THREE CORNERS

My hat it has three corners
Three corners has my hat
And had it not three corners
It would not be my hat

MY

HAT

THREE

The actions are demonstrated here by our friend Lightning. The song is repeated, and each time one of the words is omitted but the action remains. The final run through is acted out in silence.

HEAD AND SHOULDERS

(Tune : Tavern in the Town)

Head, shoulders, knees and toes, knees and toes
Head, shoulders, knees and toes, knees and toes
And eyes and ears and mouth and nose
Head, shoulders knees and toes, knees and toes

This song is best sung standing up, with the
participants indicating the parts of the body
referred to. The song can be sung over and over
again, increasing in speed, until it becomes
impossible to keep up with.

For a change, why not try singing this song in
Dutch, as follows :-

Hoofd, schouder, knie en teen, knie en teen
Hoofd, schouder, knie en teen, knie en teen
Ogen, oren, mond en neus,
Hoofd, schouder, knie en teen, knie en teen

MUSIC MAN

Leader : *(music shown with tails down)*

I am the music man and I come from down your way
And I can play

Audience : *(music shown with tails up)*

What can you play?

Leader :

I play the piano.

Audience :

Then let us hear you.

Leader :

Oh, pia-pia-piano, piano, piano
Pia-pia-piano, pia-piano.

Verse 2 :

Big bass drum - boom, boom, boom.

Verse 3 :

Triangle - ting-a-ling-a-ling.

Verse 4 :

Bagpipes - Na-na-na.

Verse 5 :

Trombone - Um-pa, um-pa, um-pa.

Verse 6 :

Viola - vio-vio-viola.

The leader and audience carry out the actions for each instrument. As each verse is sung, all the previous instruments' sounds are sung by the audience following the leader.

B-P SPIRIT

I've got that B-P spirit
Right in my head
Right in my head
Right in my head
I've got that B-P spirit right in my head
Right in my head to stay

Verse 2 :

Deep in my heart

Verse 3 :

All round my feet

Verse 4 :

I've got that B-P spirit
All over me
All over me
All over me
I've got that B-P spirit all over me
All over me to stay

This song is best sung standing up, with the participants indicating the parts of the body referred to in the song.

BLACKCROW'S SPIRIT

(Tune : John Brown's Body)

Blackcrow's spirit in the happy hunting ground
Blackcrow's spirit in the happy hunting ground
Blackcrow's spirit in the happy hunting ground
But he's ever so far away

Chorus :

Hia Hia Hiawatha
Mini mini mini ha ha
Hia Hia Hiawatha
But he's ever so far away

This song is repeated, omitting a word or words
and retaining only the action, until the final
run through is entirely silent.

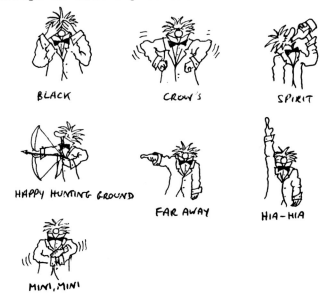

BLACK   CROW'S   SPIRIT

HAPPY HUNTING GROUND   FAR AWAY   HIA-HIA

MINI, MINI

THE GRAND OLD DUKE OF YORK

Oh, the grand old Duke of York
He had ten thousand men
He marched them up to the top of the hill
And he marched them down again
And when they were up they were up
And when they were down they were down
And when they were only half way up
They were neither up nor down

When singing about the whereabouts of the Duke
of York's men, the audience should stand, sit,
or crouch accordingly. This song may be sung
through three or four times, increasing in speed.
After this, the audience can be suitably confused
by asking them to sit when the ten thousand men
are up the hill, and to stand when they are down
the hill.

JOHN BROWN'S FLIVVER

John Brown's flivver's got a puncture in its tyre
John Brown's flivver's got a puncture in its tyre
John Brown's flivver's got a puncture in its tyre
So he mended it with chewing gum

Chorus :

Chewey, ewey, ewey, ewey etc.

This is another song in which actions gradually take the place of words, as indicated by Lightning below.

FLIVVER

PUNCTURE

CHEWEY EWEY

Just for fun

I'LL SING YOU JAM O

(Tune : Green Grow the Rushes O)

I'll sing you jam o
Green grow the rushes o
What is your jam o
Jam is jam and all the same
And ever more shall be so

Verse 2 :

I'll sing you beans o
Green grow the rushes o
Pork and beans in a little round tin
Sauce on top and in between

Verse 3 :

Marg, marg, margarine

Verse 4 :

Prunes in a sea of custard

Verse 5 :

Roast beef cooked in a baby's bath

Verse 6 :

Cocoa in the evening

Verse 7 :

Enos after every meal

THE WANDERING FLY

There was a fly who wanted to roam
So he packed his bags and left his home
Across the road to the grocery store
Where he landed on the ceiling and he landed on
                                    the floor
He landed on the sugar and he landed on the tea
And if I'd been there, he'd have landed on me

Note :

A hand clap may be inserted instead of the word
'landed' which will doubtless delight the boys!

TURNIP TOPS

You get off my turnip tops
And you get off my gate mate
If you don't run I'll get my gun
And then it'll be too late mate

(This song should be repeated faster and faster.)

MEATBALL

(Tune : On top of Old Smokey)

'Twas on the spaghetti, all covered with cheese
I lost my poor meatball, when somebody sneezed

It fell on the table and onto the floor
And then my poor meatball rolled out of the door

Out into the garden and under a bush
And then my poor meatball was nothing but mush

The very next summer there grew up a tree
And on it were meatballs to have for my tea

LEAPFROG

One hedgehog edged up the hedge as the other hedge-
hog edged down
One hedgehog edged up the hedge as the other hedge-
hog edged down
One hedgehog edged up the hedge as the other hedge-
hog edged down
As one hedgehog edged up the hedge as the other
hedgehog edged down

Chorus :

They were only playing leapfrog
They were only playing leapfrog
They were only playing leapfrog
As one hedgehog edged up the hedge as the other
hedgehog edged down

Verses :

1) A spider espyed a spider astride another spider's
back
2) One photographer photographed another photo-
grapher's back
3) One slow worm slid up the sluice as another slow
worm slid down

- 21 -

THE ANIMAL FAIR

We went to the animal fair
The birds and the beasts were there
The gay baboon by the light of the moon
Was combing his auburn hair
The monkey fell out of his bunk (bonk!)
Slid down the elephant's trunk (wheee!)
The elephant sneezed and fell on his knees
And what became of the monkey, monkey, monkey,
                                    monkey, monk
Monkey, monkey, monkey, monkey, monkey

This song can be sung in two parts. One half of
the singers keeps the tempo going with 'monkey,
monkey, monkey' while the other half sings the
verse again. Then they swap over.

WORMS

Nobody likes me, everybody hates me
Think I'll go and eat worms
Long thin skinny ones, short fat juicy ones
See how they wriggle and squirm
Bite their heads off, suck their juice out
Throw the skins away
You should see how well I thrive
On worms three times a day

YOU'LL NEVER GO TO HEAVEN

Leader   : You'll never go to heaven
              (music shown with tails down)
Response   : You'll never go to heaven
              (music shown with tails up)
Leader   : In an old Ford car
Response   : In an old Ford car
Leader   : 'Cos an old Ford car
Response   : 'Cos an old Ford car
Leader   : Won't get that far
Response   : Won't get that far

Chorus :

You'll never go to heaven in an old Ford car
'Cos an old Ford car won't get that far
I aint gonna grieve my lord no more.

I aint gonna grieve my lord
I aint gonna grieve my lord
I aint gonna grieve my lord no more

Other verses :

1. You'll never go to heaven in a ping pong ball
   'Cos a ping pong ball is much too small

2. You'll never go to heaven in a limousine
   'Cos the Lord aint got no gasoline

3. You'll never go to heaven in a Sabre Jet
   'Cos the Lord aint got no runways yet

4. You'll never go to heaven in a Girl Guide's arms
   'Cos the Lord doesn't want those feminine charms

5. You'll never go to heaven in a rocking chair
   'Cos the Lord don't want no rockers there

6. You'll never go to heaven in a wicker chair
   'Cos the Lord don't want no baskets there

7. You'll never go to heaven in a biscuit tin
   'Cos a biscuit tin's got biscuits in

8. You'll never go to heaven in an apple tree
   'Cos an apple tree's got roots you see

9. If you get there before I do
   Then dig a hole and pull me through

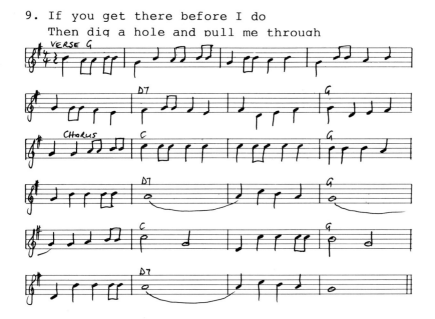

McTAVISH IS DEAD

Oh, McTavish is dead and his brother don't know it
His brother is dead and McTavish don't know it
They're both of them dead and they're in the same bed
And neither one knows that the other is dead

This song should be repeated, getting faster and faster.

THE BEAR WENT OVER THE MOUNTAIN

(Tune : For he's a jolly good fellow)

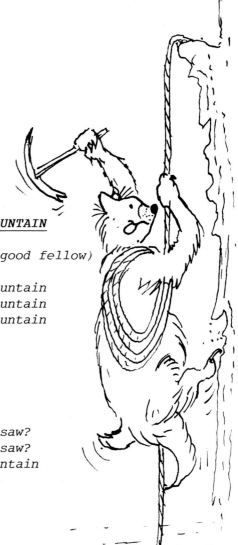

The bear went over the mountain
The bear went over the mountain
The bear went over the mountain
To see what he could see

Verse :

And what do you think he saw?
And what do you think he saw?
The other side of the mountain
Was all that he could see

AINT IT GREAT TO BE CRAZY

Chorus :

Boom, boom, ain't it great to be crazy
Boom, boom, ain't it great to be crazy
Giddy and foolish all day long
Boom, boom, ain't it great to be crazy

Way down South where bananas grow
A monkey stepped on an elephant's toe
The elephant said with tears in his eyes
"Pick on someone your own size."

Chorus

My grandfather wore a suit of underwear
He wore it 9 months without a single tear
He wore it 9 months without exaggeration
'Cos he couldn't get it off 'cos he lost the
combination

Chorus

I love me I think I'm grand
I go to the pictures and I hold my hand
I put my arms around my waist
And I get so fresh I slap my face

Chorus

I call myself on the telephone
Just to hear my golden tone
I ask myself out for a date
And I call for myself at half past eight

Chorus

A horse and a flea and three blind mice
Sitting on a tombstone playing dice
Horse he slipped and fell on the flea
Whoops! said the flea - there's a horse on me

Chorus

I'm a little acorn old and brown
I live way down in the cold, cold ground
Everybody steps on me
And that is why I'm cracked you see

Chorus

(ALTERNATIVE CHORDS: E, A, B7 WITH CAPO AT FIRST FRET.)

HE JUMPED FROM 40,000 FEET

He jumped from 40,000 feet without a parachute
He jumped from 40,000 feet without a parachute
He jumped from 40,000 feet without a parachute
And he aint gonna jump no more

They scraped him   off the   tarmac like a lump of
strawberry jam

Chorus

They put him in an envelope and sent him home to mum

Chorus

She put it on the mantlepiece for everyone to see

Chorus

The next day in the NAAFI they had strawberry jam
for tea

QUARTER MASTER'S STORES

Chorus :

My eyes are dim I cannot see
I have not brought my specs with me
I have not brought my specs with me

There were mice, mice eating all the rice
In the stores, in the stores
There were mice, mice eating all the rice
In the quarter master's stores

There was gravy, gravy enough to sink a Navy

There was soup, soup supposed to feed the group

There was meat, meat wrapped in muslin sheet

There was honey, honey melting and rather runny

There was bread, bread found in a potting shed

There was beef, beef harder than your teeth

There was cake, cake they bought it by mistake

There was fish, fish a supplementary dish

There was curry, curry but there's no need to worry

There were buns, buns bullets for the guns

There were eggs, eggs nearly growing legs

This song is frequently adapted to suit local characters and events, for example :

There was skip, skip giving us the slip.

The words should be well prepared and rehearsed before presentation.

WOAD

(Tune : Men of Harlech)

What's the use of wearing braces
Vests and pants and boots and laces
Spats or hats you buy in places
Down in Brompton Road
What's the use of shirts of cotton
Studs that always get forgotten
These affairs are simply rotten
Better far is Woad

Woad's the stuff to show men
Woad to scare your foe men
Boil it to a brilliant blue
And rub it on your back and your abdomen
Ancient Briton never hit on
Anything as good as Woad to fit on
Neck or knees or where you sit on
Tailors you be blowed

Roman came across the channel
All dressed up in tin and flannel
Half a pint of Woad per man'll
Dress us more than these
Saxons you can waste your stitches
Building beds for bugs in britches
We have Woad to clothe us which is
Not a nest for flees

Romans keep your armours
Saxons your pyjamas
Hairy coats were meant for goats
Gorillas, yaks, retriever dogs and llamas
Tramp up Snowdon with your Woad on
Never mind if we get rained or snowed on
Never want a button sewed on
Go it, ancient B's

FOUND A PEANUT

(Tune : Clementine)

Found a peanut, found a peanut, found a peanut over
there
Thought I'd eat it, thought I'd eat it, thought
I'd eat it, didn't care

Rather tasty, rather tasty, rather tasty but now
Got a pain, got a pain, got a pain, don't know how

Fetch a doctor, fetch a doctor, fetch a doctor,
fetch him quick
Appendicitis, appendicitis, appendicitis, feeling
sick

Cut him open, cut him open, cut him open, save his
life
Sew him up, sew him up, sew him up around my knife

Cut him open, cut him open, cut him open 'til it's
found
Sew him up, sew him up, have you seen my specs around

Cut him open, cut him open, cut him open - ad nauseam!

ON MULES WE FIND

(Tune : Auld Lang Syne)

On mules we find two legs behind
And two we find before
We stand behind before we find
What the two behind be for
If you stand behind the two behind
You find what they be for
So stand before the two behind
And behind the two before

SONG WITH AN UNEXPECTED ENDING

(Tune : Clementine)

I'm a teacup
I'm a teacup
I'm a teacup yes I am
But I'd rather be a teacup than a mug

I'm a bloodstain
I'm a bloodstain
I'm a bloodstain yes I am
But I'd rather be a bloodstain than a clot

I'm a moose
I'm a moose
I'm a moose yes I am
But I'd rather be a moose than a fool

I'm a raindrop
I'm a raindrop
I'm a raindrop yes I am
But I'd rather be a raindrop than a drip

I'm a mosquito
I'm a mosquito
I'm a mosquito yes I am
But I'd rather be a mosquito than a nit

Rounds and Part Songs

GILLI GILLI

A ram sam sam
A ram sam sam
Gilli, gilli, gilli, gilli
Ram sam sam

A ram sam sam
A ram sam sam
Gilli, gilli, gilli, gilli
Ram sam sam

Arami, arami
Gilli, gilli, gilli, gilli
Ram sam sam

Arami, arami
Gilli, gilli, gilli, gilli
Ram sam sam

Sing as a round in 2 or 4 parts and/or starting slowly and speeding up.

GING GANG GOO

Ging gang gooli gooli gooli watcha
Ging gang goo, ging gang goo
Ging gang gooli gooli gooli watcha
Ging gang goo, ging gang goo
Hayla - hayla shayla - hayla shayla hayla hoo
Hayla - hayla shayla - hayla shayla hayla hoo
Shally-wally,   shally-wally,   shally-wally,   shally-
                                                wally

Oompah, oompah, oompah

The singers are divided into two parts. All sing
the song through, then Part I keeps up the Oompah,
Oompah, whilst Part II starts again.   When they
meet at the end, Part I sings the words and Part II
takes over the Oompah, Oompah.

THE ZULU WARRIOR

Hold him down you Zulu warrior
Hold him down you Zulu chief
Hold him down you Zulu warrior
Hold him down you Zulu chief, chief, chief

Chorus :

I ziga zumba zumba zumba
I ziga zumba zumba zai

(repeat)

Note : The word 'chief' can be chanted by half
the singers, who then take over singing
at (A). The song can end with everybody
chanting 'chief, chief', dying away to a
whisper.

THE BATTERED ELM TREE

From out the battered elm tree
The owl's cry we hear
And from the distant forest
The cuckoo answers clear
Cuckoo, cuckoo, tu-whit, tu-whit, tu-whoo
Cuckoo, cuckoo, tu-whit, tu-whit, tu-whoo

This can be sung as a round.

ALL THINGS SHALL PERISH

All things shall perish from under the sky
All things shall perish from under the sky
Music alone shall live
Music alone shall live
Music alone shall live
Never to die

This song can be sung as a round.

TIPPERARY

It's a long way to Tipperary
It's a long way to go
It's a long, long way to Tipperary
To the sweetest girl I know
Goodbye Piccadilly
Farewell Leicester Square
It's a long, long way to Tipperary
But my heart is there

PACK UP YOUR TROUBLES

Pack up your troubles in your old kit bag and smile,
smile, smile
While you've a lucifer to light your fag smile
boys, that's the style
What's the use of worrying, it never was worth
while so
Pack up your troubles in your old kit bag and smile,
smile, smile

Note :

These two popular songs from the First World War
can be sung together as a round. If one part
starts singing "It's a long way to Tipperary"
and the other part begins "Pack up your troubles"
immediately after "It's a", then both parts should
finish singing simultaneously.

THE RATTLING BOG

Chorus :

Ro, ro the rattling bog
The bog down in the valley O
Rare bog a rattling bog
A bog down in the valley O

Verse :

And on that bog there was a tree
A rare tree, a rattling tree
The tree in the bog and the bog down in the valley O

Note :

Each subsequent verse adds one of the following
lines until by the last verse the whole song is
being sung. Once the words are known, the song
can be accelerated as it proceeds, which makes
life even more exciting.

Verse :

And on that feather there was a flea
A rare flea, a rattling flea
The flea on the feather and the feather on the wing
And the wing on the bird and the bird on the egg
And the egg on the nest and the nest on the leaf
And the leaf on the twig and the twig on the branch
And the branch on the limb and the limb on the tree
And the tree in the bog and the bog down in the
                                    valley O

Folk Songs

LAND OF THE SILVER BIRCH

Land of the silver birch, home of the beaver
Where still the mighty moose wandered at will

Chorus :

Blue lake and rocky shore, I will return once more
Boom diddi-eye-di, boom diddi-eye-di, boom diddi-
eye-di, boom

My heart is sick for you, here in the lowlands
I will return to you, hills of the north

Chorus

Swift as a silver fish, canoe of birch bark
Thy mighty waterways carry me forth

Chorus

There where the blue lake lies, I'll set my wigwam
Close to the water's edge, silent and still

Chorus

This song can be sung as a round.

GREEN GROW THE RUSHES O

I'll sing you one o
Green grow the rushes o
What is your one o
One is one and all alone
And ever more shall be so

Two, two the lily white boys
Clothed all in green o o

Three, three the rivals

Four for the Gospel makers

Five for the symbols at your door

Six for the six brown walkers

Seven for the seven stars in the sky

Eight for the April rainers

Nine for the nine bright shiners

Ten for the Ten Commandments

Eleven for the eleven that went to heaven

Twelve for the twelve apostles

THE WILD ROVER

I've been a wild rover for many the year
And I've spent all my money on whiskey and beer
And now I'm returning with gold in great store
And I never will play the wild rover no more

Chorus :

And it's no, nay, never
No, nay, never no more
Will I play the wild rover
No never no more

I went into an ale house I used to frequent
And I told the landlady my money was spent
I asked her for credit, she answered me "Nay
Sure 'tis custom like yours I can get any day"

Chorus

I took out from my pocket 10 sovereigns bright
And the landlady's eyes opened wide with delight
She said "Sir, I have whiskey and wines of the best
And the words I have spoke they were only in jest"

Chorus

I'll go home to my parents - confess what I've done
And I'll ask them to pardon their prodigal son
And then they'll caress me as oft times before
And I never will play the wild rover no more

Chorus

THE LEAVING OF LIVERPOOL

Farewell the Princes landing stage
River Mersey fare thee well
I am bound for California(y)
A place I know right well, so ...

Chorus :

Fare thee well, my own true love
When I return united we will be
It's not the leaving of Liverpool that grieves me
But my darlin' when I think on thee

I am bound for California
By way of stormy Cape Horn
And I will send thee a letter, love
When I am homeward bound

Chorus

Farewell to Lower Frederick Street
Anson Terrace and Park Lane
And it will be a long, long time
Till I see thee again

Chorus

I've shipped on board a Yankee ship
Davy Crockett is her name
And Burgess is the captain o' her
And they say she's a floating shame

Chorus

I shipped with Burgess once before
And I think I know him well
If a man's a sailor he can get along
But if not then his life is hell

Chorus

The tug is waiting at the pier
To take us down the stream
Our sails are loose and the anchor is up
And I'll say farewell once more

Chorus

SKYE BOAT SONG

Chorus :

Speed, bonny boat, like a bird on the wing
"Onward!" the sailors cry
Carry the lad that's born to be king
Over the sea to Skye

Loud the winds howl, loud the waves roar
Thunder claps rend the air
Baffled, our foes stand by the shore
Follow they will not dare

Chorus

Though the waves leap, soft Charlie sleep
The ocean's a royal bed
Rocked on the deep, Flora will keep
Watch by your weary head

Chorus

Many's the lad fought on that day
Well the claymore could wield
When the night came silently lay
Dead on Culloden's field

Chorus

Burnt are our homes; exile and death
Scatter our loyal men
Yet ere the sword's cold in its sheath
Charlie will come again

Chorus

ON ILKLEY MOOR BAR T'AT

Where hast thou been since I saw thee, I saw thee
On Ilkley Moor bar t'at
Where hast thou been since I saw, where hast thou
* been since I saw, where hast thou been since*
*   I saw thee*
On Ilkley Moor bar t'at, on Ilkley Moor bar t'at
On Ilkley Moor bar t'at

I've been a courting Mary Jane, Mary Jane
On Ilkley Moor bar t'at
I've been a courting Mary, I've been a courting
* Mary, I've been a courting Mary Jane*
On Ilkley Moor bar t'at, on Ilkley Moor bar t'at
On Ilkley Moor bar t'at

Then thou will catch thy death of cold, death of
*   cold*
On Ilkley Moor bar t'at
Then thou will catch thy death of, then thou will
* catch thy death of, then thou will catch thy*
*   death of cold*
On Ilkley Moor bar t'at, on Ilkley Moor bar t'at
On Ilkley Moor bar t'at

Then we shall have to bury thee, bury thee
On Ilkley Moor bar t'at
Then we shall have to bury, then we shall have
* to bury, then we shall have to bury thee*
On Ilkley Moor bar t'at, on Ilkley Moor bar t'at
On Ilkley Moor bar t'at

Then t'worms will come and eat thee up, eat thee up
On Ilkley Moor bar t'at
Then t'worms will come and eat thee, then t'worms
will come and eat thee, then t'worms will come and
eat thee up
On Ilkley Moor bar t'at, on Ilkley Moor bar t'at
On Ilkley Moor bar t'at

Then ducks will come and eat up t'worms
On Ilkley Moor bar t'at
Then ducks will come and eat up, then ducks will
come and eat up, then ducks will come and eat
up worms
On Ilkley Moor bar t'at, on Ilkley Moor bar t'at
On Ilkley Moor bar t'at

Then we shall come and eat up ducks, eat up ducks
On Ilkley Moor bar t'at
Then we shall come and eat up, then we shall come
and eat up, then we shall come and eat up ducks
On Ilkley Moor bar t'at, on Ilkley Moor bar t'at
On Ilkley Moor bar t'at

Then we shall all have eaten thee, eaten thee
On Ilkley Moor bar t'at
Then we shall all have eaten, then we shall all
have eaten, then we shall all have eaten thee
On Ilkley Moor bar t'at, on Ilkley Moor bar t'at
On Ilkley Moor bar t'at

Spirituals and Protest Songs

DO LORD

Do Lord, oh do Lord, oh do remember me
Oh Lordy, do lord, oh do lord, oh do remember me
Oh Lordy, do Lord, oh do Lord, oh do remember me
Look away beyond the blue

I've got a home in Glory Land that outshines the sun
I've got a home in Glory Land that outshines the sun
I've got a home in Glory Land that outshines the sun
Look away beyond the blue

I take Jesus as my Saviour, you take him too
Oh Lordy, I take Jesus as my Saviour, you take him too
I take Jesus as my Saviour, you take him too
Look away beyond the blue

JUMP DOWN TURN AROUND

*Jump down turn around
Pick a bale of cotton
Jump down turn around
Pick a bale a day*

*Oh lordy, pick a bale of cotton
Oh lordy, pick a bale a day
Oh lordy, pick a bale of cotton
Oh lordy, pick a bale a day*

Verse 3 :

*Pick a pick a pick a pick a
Pick a bale of cotton
Pick a pick a pick a pick a
Pick a bale a day*

ROCK MY SOUL

Rock my soul in the bosom of Abraham
Rock my soul in the bosom of Abraham
Rock my soul in the bosom of Abraham
Oh, rock my soul

So high, I can't get over it
So low, I can't get under it
So wide, I can't get round it
Oh, rock my soul

WE SHALL NOT BE MOVED

We shall not, we shall not be moved
We shall not, we shall not be moved
Just like a tree that's standing by the water's side
We shall not be moved

Well, we're on our way to heaven
We shall not be moved
We're on our way to heaven
We shall not be moved

CHORUS

Verse 2 :

We're on that road to freedom

Verse 3 :

We are brothers together

Verse 4 :

We're on our way to heaven

WE SHALL OVERCOME

We shall overcome
We shall overcome
We shall overcome some day
Oh deep in my heart (oh lordy)
I do believe
We shall overcome some day

SWING LOW SWEET CHARIOT

Chorus :

Swing low sweet chariot
Coming for to carry me home
Swing low sweet chariot
Coming for to carry me home

I looked over Jordan and what did I see
Coming for to carry me home
A band of angels coming after me
Coming for to carry me home

Chorus

If you get there before I do
Coming for to carry me home
Tell all my friends I'm coming too
Coming for to carry me home

Chorus

The brightest day that ever I saw
Coming for to carry me home
When Jesus washed my sins away
Coming for to carry me home

Chorus

I'm sometimes up and sometimes down
Coming for to carry me home
But still my soul feels heavenly bound
Coming for to carry me home

Chorus

Yells

THE FROG AND THE STEAMROLLER

One half of the camp fire circle is delegated to represent the frog and the other half is a steamroller. The "frogs" are asked to make a loud croaking noise whenever the camp fire Leader points to them and the "steamroller" makes a loud hissing noise when the camp fire Leader points to that side of the fire.

The camp fire Leader explains that a frog is trying to cross the road and the steamroller is coming up behind him. As he tells the story he points to the frog group and then to the steamroller group with increasing regularity, until they are croaking and hissing almost in unison. At the last moment the Leader raises his hand and brings it down sharply and everybody in the circle makes a loud squidgy noise as the two meet and the inevitable happens.

BOOMALACKA

Boomalacka, boomalacka, bow wow wow
Chingalacka, chingalacka, chow, chow, chow
Boomalacka
Chingalacka
Who are we?
(Name of Scout Group).   Can't you see!

OGGY, OGGY, OGGY

Leader :	Oggy, oggy, oggy
Audience :	Oi, oi, oi
Leader :	Oggy, oggy, oggy
Audience :	Oi, oi, oi
Leader :	Oggy
Audience :	Oi
Leader :	Oggy
Audience :	Oi
Leader :	Oggy, oggy, oggy
Audience :	Oi, oi, oi

Index

Page No.

Index

TITLES IN THE SERIES BY PRINTFORCE:

Campfire Stunts by David Saint	£1.95
Campfire Stunts 2 by David Saint	£1.95
Campfire Songs by David Saint	£2.75
Campfire Songs 2 by Paul Taylor	£2.75
Campfire Companion by David Saint	£1.95
Group Fund Raising by David Saint	£3.95
A Year of Programme Planning by David Saint	£3.25
Recipes & Planning for Camp Cooking by David Saint	£2.75
Wide Games by David Saint	£2.75
Make It Simple by Jean Barrow	£2.75
Organised Chaos by Brian Thurston	£1.95
Outdoor Adventure by David Saint	£2.75
Get to Know . . . Nature by Jean Barrow	£2.75
Campfire Fun by David Saint	£1.95
Let's Go Cooking by Barbara Saint	£1.95
Let's Integrate by Doctor Roger May	£3.95
Let's Go Gardening by Pat Taylor and Evelyn Andrews	£2.75
Storytime by Hazel Addis	£2.75
Storytime — Audio Tape	£3.95
The Printforce Book of Challenges by David Saint	£2.75
Let's Play These Games by Frances Lane	£1.95
Let's Play These Games Two by Frances Lane	£1.95
Let's Make Music by Alex Whinnom	£1.95
Let's Pray by Lillian Ruxton	£1.95
Outdoor Organised Chaos by Brian Thurston	£1.95
Let's Get Publicity by David Saint	£3.95
Really Wet Games by Dave Wood	£1.95
Simple Ciphers by Frances Lane	£3.25
Let's Go Green by Lora A. Lisbon	£3.95
Think Themes, by Frances Lane	£2.75
D.I.Y. Training Resources by Dave Wood and Dave Ludlow	£2.75
On With Your Show by Ron Meyer	£3.95

More titles to follow. All titles + 35p P & P

6 Angel Hill Drive
Sutton
Surrey SM1 3BX